Medieval
Gardens

ADDRESS BOOK

name Aronson E. / T. Belliveau
address 14 Oak Terrace, Box 475
Mapleville, R.I. 02839-0475
tel

name Atwater, Kay
address 524 Fearington Post
Pittsboro, N.C. 27312
tel 919 542 - 6819

name
address

tel

name
address

tel

name Academy of music
address

tel 215 893 -1930

A room with a summer's view

name

address

tel

name

address

tel

name

address

tel

name

address

tel

name

address

tel

name

address

tel

name

address

tel

name

address

tel

name

address

tel

name

address

tel

name

address

tel

name

address

tel

Cerasia, sap. aut
cerexia.

cera citrina.

B

name Belliveau, Craig
address 812 Saturn Ct.
 Marco Island, Fl. 33937
tel

name Berg, Betty
address 174 Meadowbrook Dr.
 H.V., Pa. 19006-6850
tel 215 Wi. 7-0103

name Beere, Nancy
address 200 Locust St. 12 D
 Phila., Pa. 19106
tel 215 Wa.2-3670

name Brock, Scotty + Hugh
address RD. # 2, Box 457
 Elverson, Pa. 19520
tel 610 286-0602

name Barrow, Boyd + Betic Jean
address Rt. # 2, Box 288
 Snow Hill, N.C. 28580
tel

Picking cherries

name Betz, Diane + Fred Jr.
address 1433 Greenawalt. Rd.
H.V., Pa. 19006
tel

name Behmy, Bob + Rich/Emmons
address 243 Almshouse Rd.
Doylestown, Pa. 18901
tel 215 348-0917

name Berry, Isobel + David
address
Phila., Pa. 19119
tel 248-3589 (H)
248-9361 or 247-2103 (W)

name Banister, Eleanor
address 3484 Heather Rd.
H.V., Pa. 19006
tel 215 Wi.7-3964

name Behm, Joanne + Bill Severson
address 103 Rockland
Narberth, Pa. 19072
tel 610 664-5502

name Bass, Susan
address

tel Mo 5-3423

name Benton, Vance + Greg
address 300 Rolling Oaks Dr., apt. 298
Thousand Oak, Ca 91361
tel 805-494-4418

name Buchanan, Sue L. + Jerry
address 4318 Atlantic Ave.
Brooklyn, N.Y. 11224-1026
tel 718·449-4278

name
address

tel

name
address

tel

name
address

tel

name
address

tel

name _Crawford, Jackie + Bill_
address _73 Willow St._
Westwood, Ma. 02090
tel _____

name _Cox, Alene_
address _103 Red Pt. Dr. Rt.#10_
Smithfield, Va. 23430
tel _804 357-4868_

name _Clark, J.A. (Jo)_
address _1548 Cross Keys Ct._
Richmond, Va.
tel _____

name _____
address _____
_____
tel _____

name _____
address _____
_____
tel _____

name _____

address _____

_____

tel _____

name _____

address _____

_____

tel _____

name _____

address _____

_____

tel _____

name _____

address _____

_____

tel _____

name _____

address _____

_____

tel _____

name _____

address _____

_____

tel _____

name

address

tel

name

address

tel

name

address

tel

name

address

tel

name

address

tel

name

address

tel

name Dimmig, Carolyn + Don
address 1184 Wright Dr.
H.V., Pa. 19006
tel 215 WI.7-0106

name Durban, Penny, Charlie + Brian
address 13955 Marygold, Ct.
Chesterfield, Mo. 63017
tel 314 878 - 2443

name Di Giovanni, Mary
address 30 Deborah Drive
Reading, Ma. 01867
tel 617 944 - 5150

name
address

tel

name
address

tel

Tending the manor lawn

name

address

tel

name

address

tel

name

address

tel

name

address

tel

name

address

tel

name

address

tel

name _____
address _____
_____
tel _____

name _____
address _____
_____
tel _____

name _____
address _____
_____
tel _____

name _____
address _____
_____
tel _____

name _____
address _____
_____
tel _____

name _____
address _____
_____
tel _____

name Elser, Liz + Veit Tilly, Nicky Toby
address 22 Eagleshead Rd.
Ithaca, N.Y. 14850
tel 607 539-6707
Nickolas, Tihlman, Tobias

name Earussi, Pam
address 889 Stonybrook Ln.
Lansdale, Pa. 19446
tel

name Emberger, Cass + Paul
address

tel 201·842-4992

name Epstein, Marv
address

tel 215-233-1953

name Entrekin
address

tel 610-286·8866

A miller scything

name _____
address _____
_____
tel _____

name _____
address _____
_____
tel _____

name _____
address _____
_____
tel _____

name _____
address _____
_____
tel _____

name _____
address _____
_____
tel _____

name _____
address _____
_____
tel _____

name

address

tel

name

address

tel

name

address

tel

name

address

tel

name

address

tel

name

address

tel

F

name Feinstein, Barbara
address 435 E. Lancaster Ave. #211
St. Davids, Pa. 19087
tel (610) 688-5579

name Fleck, Betty Lou & Jack
address 48-425 Via Solana
La Quinta, Ca. 92253
tel (619) 771-2544
(508)-693-6009

name Fleck, Linda
address
New Hope, Pa.
tel (215) 862-5613

name Fabian, Frank J. & Patty
address 7159 Koldyke Dr.
Fishers, Ind. 46038
tel (313) 486-3293

name French, Maggie
address 303 Crestline Blvd.
Greenville, N.C. 27834-6817
tel

Shearing sheep on a summer's day

name Findlay, Sue + Ian
address 17 Black St.
Stoke, Nelson, N.Z.
tel

name Feeney, Tom r Betty
address

tel (215) 362-7963

name
address

tel

name
address

tel

name
address

tel

name
address

tel

name

address

tel

name

address

tel

name

address

tel

name

address

tel

name

address

tel

name

address

tel

G

---

name_____
address_____
_____
tel_____

---

name_____
address_____
_____
tel_____

---

name_____
address_____
_____
tel_____

---

name_____
address_____
_____
tel_____

---

name_____
address_____
_____
tel_____

Peasants sowing seeds

name _____
address _____
_____
tel _____

name _____
address _____
_____
tel _____

name _____
address _____
_____
tel _____

name _____
address _____
_____
tel _____

name _____
address _____
_____
tel _____

name _____
address _____
_____
tel _____

name

address

tel

name

address

tel

name

address

tel

name

address

tel

name

address

tel

name

address

tel

De sancto sebastiano anti.

 mia refulsit gratia sebastia
nus martir inclitus: qui militis potens
insignia: sed & fratrum palma sollicit?
confortauit corda trementia verbo sibi
collato celitus. versus. Ora pro nobis bte
sebastiane. R. Vt meramur pestem
epidimie illesi pertransire et promissio
nem xpi obtinere. Oratio.

Deus qui beatum sebastia
num martyrem tuum in
tua fide et dilectione tam ardenter so
lidasti: vt nullis carnalibus blandi
mentis: nullis tyrannorum immi
nullisq carnificum gladiis siue sa
gittis aut tormentis a tua cultura
potuit reuocari: da nobis in istam
precatoribus dignis eius meritis et
intercessionibus: in tribulatione au
xilium: in persecutione solatium: et
in omni tempore contra pestem epi
dimie remedium: quatinus possim?

name _____
address _____
_____
tel _____

name _____
address _____
_____
tel _____

name _____
address _____
_____
tel _____

name _____
address _____
_____
tel _____

name _____
address _____
_____
tel _____

Poppies and dragonflies

name

address

tel

name

address

tel

name

address

tel

name

address

tel

name

address

tel

name

address

tel

name _____

address _____

tel _____

name _____

address _____

tel _____

name _____

address _____

tel _____

name _____

address _____

tel _____

name _____

address _____

tel _____

name _____

address _____

tel _____

I

name_____
address_____
_____
tel_____

name_____
address_____
_____
tel_____

name_____
address_____
_____
tel_____

name_____
address_____
_____
tel_____

name_____
address_____
_____
tel_____

The June harvest in full swing

name

address

tel

name

address

tel

name

address

tel

name

address

tel

name

address

tel

name

address

tel

name

address

tel

name

address

tel

name

address

tel

name

address

tel

name

address

tel

name

address

tel

name
address

tel

name
address

tel

name
address

tel

name
address

tel

name
address

tel

Grape gathering

name

address

tel

name

address

tel

name

address

tel

name

address

tel

name

address

tel

name

address

tel

name _____
address _____
_____
tel _____

name _____
address _____
_____
tel _____

name _____
address _____
_____
tel _____

name _____
address _____
_____
tel _____

name _____
address _____
_____
tel _____

name _____
address _____
_____
tel _____

Castozeum

K

name _____
address _____

tel _____

name _____
address _____

tel _____

name _____
address _____

tel _____

name _____
address _____

tel _____

name _____
address _____

tel _____

A young girl at the pond

name _____

address _____

_____

tel _____

name _____

address _____

_____

tel _____

name _____

address _____

_____

tel _____

name _____

address _____

_____

tel _____

name _____

address _____

_____

tel _____

name _____

address _____

_____

tel _____

name

address

tel

name

address

tel

name

address

tel

name

address

tel

name

address

tel

name

address

tel

name _____
address _____
_____
tel _____

name _____
address _____
_____
tel _____

name _____
address _____
_____
tel _____

name _____
address _____
_____
tel _____

name _____
address _____
_____
tel _____

The harvesters' meal

name

address

tel

name

address

tel

name

address

tel

name

address

tel

name

address

tel

name

address

tel

name

address

tel

name

address

tel

name

address

tel

name

address

tel

name

address

tel

name

address

tel

M

name
address

tel

name
address

tel

name
address

tel

name
address

tel

name
address

tel

Ploughing the land

name

address

tel

name

address

tel

name

address

tel

name

address

tel

name

address

tel

name

address

tel

name

address

tel

name

address

tel

name

address

tel

name

address

tel

name

address

tel

name

address

tel

name _____
address _____
_____
tel _____

name _____
address _____
_____
tel _____

name _____
address _____
_____
tel _____

name _____
address _____
_____
tel _____

name _____
address _____
_____
tel _____

Medieval landscaping

name

address

tel

name

address

tel

name

address

tel

name

address

tel

name

address

tel

name

address

tel

name

address

tel

name

address

tel

name

address

tel

name

address

tel

name

address

tel

name

address

tel

name _____
address _____
_____
tel _____

name _____
address _____
_____
tel _____

name _____
address _____
_____
tel _____

name _____
address _____
_____
tel _____

name _____
address _____
_____
tel _____

Scenes from garden labour

name

address

tel

name

address

tel

name

address

tel

name

address

tel

name

address

tel

name

address

tel

name

address

tel

---

name

address

tel

---

name

address

tel

---

name

address

tel

---

name

address

tel

---

name

address

tel

name_____
address_____
_____
tel_____

name_____
address_____
_____
tel_____

name_____
address_____
_____
tel_____

name_____
address_____
_____
tel_____

name_____
address_____
_____
tel_____

Relaxing on a summer day

name

address

tel

name

address

tel

name

address

tel

name

address

tel

name

address

tel

name

address

tel

name _____
address _____
_____
tel _____

name _____
address _____
_____
tel _____

name _____
address _____
_____
tel _____

name _____
address _____
_____
tel _____

name _____
address _____
_____
tel _____

name _____
address _____
_____
tel _____

name

address

tel

name

address

tel

name

address

tel

name

address

tel

name

address

tel

Horses at work on the land

name

address

tel

---

name

address

tel

---

name

address

tel

---

name

address

tel

---

name

address

tel

---

name

address

tel

name

address

tel

name

address

tel

name

address

tel

name

address

tel

name

address

tel

name

address

tel

name _____
address _____
_____
tel _____

name _____
address _____
_____
tel _____

name _____
address _____
_____
tel _____

name _____
address _____
_____
tel _____

name _____
address _____
_____
tel _____

The garden of love

name

address

tel

name

address

tel

name

address

tel

name

address

tel

name

address

tel

name

address

tel

name _____
address _____
_____
tel _____

name _____
address _____
_____
tel _____

name _____
address _____
_____
tel _____

name _____
address _____
_____
tel _____

name _____
address _____
_____
tel _____

name _____
address _____
_____
tel _____

name

address

tel

name

address

tel

name

address

tel

name

address

tel

name

address

tel

Falconry, haymaking and chasing butterflies

name

address

tel

name

address

tel

name

address

tel

name

address

tel

name

address

tel

name

address

tel

name

address

tel

name

address

tel

name

address

tel

name

address

tel

name

address

tel

name

address

tel

name _____
address _____

tel _____

name _____
address _____

tel _____

name _____
address _____

tel _____

name _____
address _____

tel _____

name _____
address _____

tel _____

The garden through all seasons

name

address

tel

name

address

tel

name

address

tel

name

address

tel

name

address

tel

name

address

tel

name _____
address _____
_____
tel _____

name _____
address _____
_____
tel _____

name _____
address _____
_____
tel _____

name _____
address _____
_____
tel _____

name _____
address _____
_____
tel _____

name _____
address _____
_____
tel _____

name _____

address _____

_____

tel _____

name _____

address _____

_____

tel _____

name _____

address _____

_____

tel _____

name _____

address _____

_____

tel _____

name _____

address _____

_____

tel _____

Lovers in spring

name_____
address_____
_____
tel_____

name_____
address_____
_____
tel_____

name_____
address_____
_____
tel_____

name_____
address_____
_____
tel_____

name_____
address_____
_____
tel_____

name_____
address_____
_____
tel_____

name

address

tel

name

address

tel

name

address

tel

name

address

tel

name

address

tel

name

address

tel

name_____
address_____
_____
tel_____

name_____
address_____
_____
tel_____

name_____
address_____
_____
tel_____

name_____
address_____
_____
tel_____

name_____
address_____
_____
tel_____

Taking lunch

name
address

tel

name
address

tel

name
address

tel

name
address

tel

name
address

tel

name
address

tel

name

address

tel

name

address

tel

name

address

tel

name

address

tel

name

address

tel

name

address

tel

W

name _____
address _____

tel _____

name _____
address _____

tel _____

name _____
address _____

tel _____

name _____
address _____

tel _____

name _____
address _____

tel _____

My lord and his lady

name_____
address_____
_____
tel_____

name_____
address_____
_____
tel_____

name_____
address_____
_____
tel_____

name_____
address_____
_____
tel_____

name_____
address_____
_____
tel_____

name_____
address_____
_____
tel_____

name

address

tel

name

address

tel

name

address

tel

name

address

tel

name

address

tel

name

address

tel

name

address

tel

name

address

tel

name

address

tel

name

address

tel

name

address

tel

The mythical garden

Picture credits

p2 and cover: *Master of the Embroidered Leaf,* 15th century, Private Collection (ph: Bridgeman). p6: *Picking Cherries,* Compendium of Medieval Gardens, British Library Ms. 4016, fol. 108 (Ph: Bridgeman). p10: *July,* The Bedford Hours, British Library (Ph: Bridgeman). p14: Les Très Riches Heures du Duc de Berry, 15th century, Private Collection (Ph: Bridgeman). p18: *June,* The Bedford Hours, British Library (Ph: Bridgeman). p22: *Shearing Sheep,* Benninck Book of Hours, British Library (Ph: Bridgeman). p26: *Sowing the seed,* Le Rustican c.1460 (Ph: Bridgeman). p34: *June Harvest,* Benninck Book of Hours, British Library, Ms. 18855 fol. 109 (Ph: Bridgeman). p38: *Grape Gathering,* Le Rustican, Musée Condee (Ph: Bridgeman). p42: *The Young Woman and the Unicorn,* Les Livres des Simples Médecines, Bibliotèque National Ms 12322 fol. 188 (Ph: Bridgeman). p46: *Harvesting,* Benninck Book of Hours, Victoria and Albert Museum (Ph: Bridgeman). p54: *Harvesting,* Le Rustican c, 1460, Musée Condée (Ph: Bridgeman). p58: *Scenes from the Labours of the Year,* Musée Condée (Ph: Bridgeman). p62: *Dream Enters the Garden,* Hadley Ms, British Library Ms. 4425, fol. 12 (Ph: Bridgeman). p66: *Ploughing and Sowing,* Benninck, of Hours, Victoria and Albert Museum (Ph: Bridgeman). p70: *Emblems and Devices of Love,* Stowe Ms. 95 fol. 12, British Library (Ph: Bridgeman). p74: Flemish Calendar, British Library Ms. 24098 fol. 24 (Ph: Bridgeman). p78: *Scenes from the labours of the year,* Musée Condée (Ph: Bridgeman). p82: *The Month of April,* Benninck Book of Hours, Victoria and Albert Museum (Ph: Bridgeman). p86: *Corn Harvest, Cock Throwing,* Flemish Calendar, British Library MS. 24098 fol. 25 (Ph: Bridgeman). p90: *April,* Flemish Calendar, British Library (Ph: Bridgeman)

CLB 4613
Published exclusively for
PAST TIMES
by CLB Publishing Limited
Godalming Business Centre, Woolsack Way,
Godalming, Surrey GU7 1XW
Copyright © CLB Publishing 1995

Designed by Tim Scott
Typeset by Spectrum Typesetting Ltd
Printed in Hong Kong

ISBN 1-85833-475-6